Benjamin Britten

Te Deum in C

FULL SCORE

MUSIC DEPARTMENT

OXFORD
UNIVERSITY PRESS

OXFORD
UNIVERSITY PRESS

Great Clarendon Street, Oxford OX2 6DP, England
198 Madison Avenue, New York, NY10016, USA

Oxford University Press is a department of the University of Oxford.
It furthers the University's aim of excellence in research, scholarship,
and education by publishing worldwide

Oxford is a registered trade mark of Oxford University Press
in the UK and in certain other countries

© Oxford University Press 2002

The moral rights of the author have been asserted
Database right Oxford University Press (maker)

First published 2002

All rights reserved. No part of this publication may be reproduced,
stored in a retrieval system, or transmitted, in any form or by any means,
without the prior permission in writing of Oxford University Press,
or as expressly permitted by law. Enquiries concerning reproduction
outside the scope of the above should be sent to the Music Copyright
Department, Oxford University Press, at the address above

Permission to perform this work in public
(except in the course of divine worship) should normally be obtained
from the Performing Right Society Ltd. (PRS), 29/33 Berners Street,
London W1T 3AB, or its affiliated Societies in each country throughout
the world, unless the owner or the occupier of the premises
being used holds a licence from the Society

Permission to make a recording must be obtained in advance
from the Mechanical Copyright Protection Society Ltd. (MCPS),
Elgar House, 41 Streatham High Road, London SW16 1ER,
or its affiliated Societies in each country throughout the world

1 3 5 7 9 10 8 6 4 2

ISBN 0-19-351524-5

Music and text origination by
Halstan & Co. Ltd., Amersham, Bucks.
Printed in Great Britain on acid-free paper by
Caligraving Ltd., Thetford, Norfolk

Benjamin Britten

Te Deum in C

for

treble solo, SATB choir, harp, and strings

FULL SCORE

INTRODUCTION

Britten would never again be as unambiguously 'religious' as he was in the 1920s and 1930s after which a wider spiritualism gradually replaced his allegiance to the institutional Church of his upbringing and schooling. Moreover, in his later life he did not shy away from questioning the basis of religious belief in a society that kills and goes to war, sometimes in God's name. The *War Requiem*, with its ironic juxtaposition of Wilfred Owen's war poetry and the liturgy of the requiem mass, is only the most obvious example. But no such irony played a part in his religious music of the 1930s. It served either a strict liturgical function—the Te Deum in C (1934), the Jubilate Deo in E flat (1934), and a few sketched but unfinished pieces—or aligned itself with traditional religious iconography and imagery—*A Hymn to the Virgin* (1930; revised 1934), *The Sycamore Tree* (1930; revised 1934 and 1967), and *Christ's Nativity* (1931), a precursor to *A Boy was Born* (1933). Each of these, whether an extended narrative or a brilliant miniature, depicts key aspects of early Christian history.

The rationale behind the works in the second of the above groups is straightforward enough—each is a boy's own story, a reiteration of childhood beliefs, centred on the boy Christ and his earthly parents. As such, the poems slip easily into the eclectic, if conservative, library of texts set by Britten in the 1920s and early 1930s. Those in the first group, though, were composed through slightly different motivation. These were almost the first fruits of the young *professional* composer, who was by now earning his living through his music, and in these works was identifying and supplying a mass market. The music department of Oxford University Press, only eleven years old in 1934, was doing exactly the same thing during this period: schools, community choirs, and naturally churches were on its list. Thus, composer and publisher shared mutually beneficial aims. Yet neither party could be accused of cynically exploiting existing markets for commercial gain; it is simply that in these works Britten's religious beliefs coincided with his professional needs and opportunities.

The orchestral version of the Te Deum, composed originally with organ accompaniment, grew out of this emerging professionalism and was evidence of the adaptability that would, in this exact period, form the basis of Britten's reputation. Commissioned by the BBC, which was already taking a keen interest in his music, the work was premièred in a Lemare concert, then a vital forum for new music, in January 1936, a little over a year after the original version had been completed. In retrospect, the première takes on a significance little understood at the time, for the orchestra included in its ranks Britten on viola and was directed by the young choir trainer Reginald Goodall, who less than ten years later would conduct the first performance of *Peter Grimes*.

Perhaps understandably, given the work's primary liturgical function, the orchestral version made little headway, while the original Te Deum, for choir and organ, was quickly absorbed into the mainstream of English church music. Both contain a number of features shared by other Britten choral works of the time: the slow harmonic pulse (the first fifty-or-so bars are built on C major triads) in an allegro tempo is one feature of the finale to *A Boy Was Born*; the chromatic treble solo over a simple choral texture in the section 'Thou art the King of Glory, O Christ' had also been tried out in *A Boy Was Born*, as had the juxtaposition of unrelated key areas, used here to great effect to demarcate different sections of text.

Britten did not include text in his fair copy of this version, and neither did he write in every vocal detail. Consequently, the vocal part in this score is taken from the earlier choir and organ version. However, in preparing this orchestral score for publication, it became clear that there were a number of discrepancies between Britten's manuscript and the original 1935 vocal score. Some of these were minor: different articulation and dynamic markings, something Britten was later very fussy about, but perhaps left unchanged on proof because of his relative inexperience at this stage of his career with the processes of music publishing. Yet some were more important: wrong pedal notes, for example, which Britten failed to notice on proof, and which have been perpetuated in performances and recordings for nearly seventy years. These have been corrected here (Britten clearly used the published score to prepare his orchestral version) and in the new edition of the vocal score. The two versions have been made consistent in other details—the introduction of rehearsal cues and bar numbers, for example—since Britten intended choristers to use the vocal score to perform the orchestral version. This would have been an easy task, for there is little discrepancy in essential details between versions (a rare departure occurs in bars 53 to 56, where the words 'Lord God of Sabaoth' are unaccompanied in the orchestral version, but doubled by organ in the original). Sustained organ chords are often filled out with arpeggiated string writing, while the spacing of chords is frequently much wider in the string version, with melodies transposed into different octaves. Although harmony in both versions is identical, voice leading is sometimes altered in the latter to make it better suited to the idioms of instruments concerned.

So, although in essence the two versions are the same, the soundworld explored in each is quite distinct. As this new edition proves, Britten's orchestral version should neither be viewed as an occasional piece nor considered solely a liturgical work; like many of his choral pieces from the 1930s and 1940s, it is equally at home in church and concert hall.

Paul Kildea
Aldeburgh 2001

Vocal scores are available for sale.
Orchestral parts are available from the publisher's hire library.

Duration: *c.*8 minutes

Te Deum in C

BENJAMIN BRITTEN
(1913–1976)

A version with organ accompaniment and choral parts that correspond exactly to those reproduced here is available for sale (ISBN 0-19-351521-0).

© 1934 and 2002 Oxford University Press

Printed in Great Britain

OXFORD UNIVERSITY PRESS, MUSIC DEPARTMENT, GREAT CLARENDON STREET, OXFORD OX2 6DP
Photocopying this copyright material is ILLEGAL.

⊕ If there is a large number of strings the harp part may be omitted from here until 𝄋

40